A Guided
Anxiety Journal
Designed for Young Adults

Introduction

Angela Stephens is a self-made entrepreneur, an advocate for helping others and a Mother of an ADHD child. Mrs. Stephens is the CEO & Co-Founder of RE-Focus the Creative Office, as well as the Host of the Podcast: "RE-Focus with Angela Stephens" where you can listen free at www.time2refocus.com/podcast.

Angela is the President of A. Stephens & Associates, LLC, a 30 year Executive Search Firm in the C-Suite levels of the Pharmaceutical, Biotech, Food & Nutrition Industry, and the Co-Founder of DDA West Coast Productions.

RE-Focus The Creative Office is certified as a Woman Owned Business with WBENC. She is involved with various organizations and served twelve years with CASA (Court Appointed Special Advocates) to help children in Foster Care. In addition, she served as Vice President and President during her term.

Mrs. Stephens has had life experiences that have led her to creating this journal. A single parent for ten years, she learned many life lessons. Her child was diagnosed in the 5th grade with ADHD. Mrs. Stephens was diagnosed at age 45. She understands the challenges of ADHD, as well as Anxiety which has provided a broad look of the challenges of not only ADHD, but symptoms of Anxiety. This is a guided journal designed to help those feeling lost to have a resource that helps them through difficult stages in their life, while becoming encouraged. This guided journal is based on experiences from Angela Stephens who is not a Physician or Counselor, rather a Mother, an Entrepreneur, and someone who makes it a priority to show kindness, encourage others, and inspire individuals to have the best life they can imagine.

Angela Stephens is a Graduate of Drury University, and lives with her husband Darold Sauber, the COO of RE-Focus The Creative Office and son Drake Stephens, who are both Co-Founders of RE-Focus The Creative Office.

A guided journal
uniquely designed
for you.

This journal is designed to help you refocus on your journey. Feel free to advance to certain questions, as some may not apply or may be too emotional to answer. This is your journey, and it is my sincerest desire for you to have the best life possible.

If you find yourself going through a difficult time, I can't wait to help you discover a place of inner peace. Life on a daily basis can sometimes be challenging, stressful, sad, and overwhelming. However with this journal, it is my greatest wish for you to find your new journey and you feel as though we are having a conversation.

Remember to always... take a moment... and RE-Focus on YOU.

Angela Stephens

Do just ONE thing to make someone's day AMAZING!!

This is your journey.
It's not a race.
You are already a winner.

Many famous people have gone through trials, frustrations, sadness, rejection and betrayal.

"It's how you respond to what happens to you that matters."

If you are calm, others will usually return the conversation with a calm tone. If not, maybe choose a different time to talk to them.

You find out that the person you really liked was <u>fonder</u> of your friend...

Everyone has experienced hurt.

And these situations really hurt. How did you feel inside when you found out?

_____

_____

_____

_____

_____

_____

_____

_____

_____

_____

_____

_____

_____

_____

_____

If this has happened to you, I am so sorry. My heart hurts for you. I have experienced that, and that pain is indescribable...

If you feel like you are not as talented, or as good looking as that other person write out the reasons why...

_____

_____

_____

_____

_____

_____

_____

_____

_____

_____

_____

_____

_____

_____

_____

_____

_____

_____

Looking back on your life
in ten years, these things
won't matter.

They just won't.

Do you ever feel like you are *not* good enough... or you don't fit in?

We have all felt that way at one point or another in our lifetime. Know this, *you are good enough.* You have more talent inside you that you are not even aware of. Write them down.

_____

_____

_____

_____

_____

_____

_____

_____

_____

_____

_____

_____

_____

I spoke to a College Freshman who made the statement that he had met a new person almost every day. In High School, he remembered how difficult some days were. Looking back, he commented that the little things that happened then didn't matter today.

When I can't talk to anyone...

Does this picture remind you of something you are going through right now?

If it does, my heart is with you. Write down what this picture says to you below. When I saw this picture of this girl, it reminded me of myself when I was in High School.

_____
_____
_____
_____
_____
_____
_____
_____
_____
_____
_____
_____
_____
_____

If life is good for you now, does it remind you of someone? If so, maybe you could help make their world a bit better. Send them a note, text, or even a handwritten card.

Stress

Look at this stress meter. Put an X on the photo regarding where you feel right this moment.

Change everything you can.

Small things, become BIG things. When we let small things fester, they grow. Our mind races and the next thing you know, your mind is creating things that may or may not happen. List what stresses you out, have a plan on how to handle your stress:

Stress: _____

Plan: _____

_____

_____

_____

Stress: _____

Plan: _____

_____

_____

_____

Stress: _____

Plan: _____

_____

_____

_____

"I had a Physician tell me once that he sensed something was wrong. He didn't ask any other questions but told me to go home, write out everything that was wrong in my life....and change it. I went home and did just what you are doing now."

Look at the list of things that are stressful to you. Write down what you can change today in each of those areas:

Family:_____

_____

_____

_____

_____

_____

School: _____

_____

_____

_____

_____

_____

Relationships: _____

_____

_____

_____

_____

_____

This is your life and your journey.

If you were your very best friend, what would your friend tell you to do at this very minute?

_____

_____

_____

_____

_____

_____

If you had no concerns, no strings keeping you in your situation, what would you do? Where would you go? What would you be?

_____

_____

_____

_____

_____

_____

Life seems so big... yet life can be exactly how you want it to be.

"We only let our life control us if we let it."

You are important!

It is a proven fact that stress can be harmful to you mentally and physically. It's important to understand what's going on in your life.

There are things you can do now to prevent having stress. One of those things is to plan how you can handle peer pressure in group situations...

If someone makes you feel uncomfortable, what could you do to prevent that from happening? Write those ideas down:

_____

_____

_____

_____

_____

Ways to prevent stress around friends when I am uncomfortable:

_____

_____

_____

_____

_____

_____

What makes you happy?

Have you ever laughed, I mean really laughed, so hard you started crying? If so, when was that? Do you remember how you felt at that very moment?

Write down what made you laugh. Who made you laugh? Who were you with? Laughter is healing, it's a release and it puts a smile on our face.

_____

_____

_____

_____

_____

_____

_____

_____

_____

_____

_____

_____

_____

Who makes you happy?

_____

_____

_____

_____

_____

_____

_____

_____

_____

_____

_____

_____

_____

_____

_____

_____

_____

I have a photo of three people in my office. The photo was taken on a film set and I remember how that day was so perfect. When I see that photo, it makes me so happy...

If you have a picture of a great time with a friend, parent, or a pet, paste that picture here.

That's a memory you don't want to forget.

Parents

When it comes to parents, sometimes you don't want to talk to them, or tell them what's really going on in life...

Have you wondered why your parents are so hard on you? The answer sometimes is very simple... They just want you to be the best you can be but overall to be happy...

They might push you in sports, or to get better grades. They may push you to practice your instrument more. They might push you to try to get certain scholarships.

They are not being unkind... They want to push you to be the very best so that you can have an amazing life... or get into a college that you really want.

Maybe it's a life that they have envisioned for you...

However, if it's not in your vision or if it's not your desire, you should try to find a way to talk to them about that now versus later.

Research shows that in some cases, some parents will push their children, to do better because they were unable to have these things.

Maybe they arrived from another country and wanted you to have what they didn't have. If that is the case, I am sure it was a very difficult journey for them. They know that pain, and that hardship is real. They just don't want you to go through that.

Maybe their parents didn't have the resources to help them do the things that you are doing now. Maybe their parents didn't encourage them. If you go back and look at that parent's childhood, they might have wished their parents had been harder on them.

I know this may sound confusing, but it's very simple, they truly just want the best for you because they know you are not able to see what could be in your future because you are not there yet.

I knew one individual who really wanted to play a professional sport. This person did not have the support from their parents and today as that person is older, looking back they wished that their parents would have pushed them. So, as you can see by this one example, if your parents are pushing you, it may be a gift.

The next time, your parents push you to practice more, I know it's hard, but try to understand why they are doing that. They just want you to be great. They want you to be the very best you can be...

Many parents will love you no matter what...

Talk. To. Them.

Overall? They want YOU to be happy. They don't want you to be sad, or depressed, or to have anxiety. They may be facing those things today. What they really want for you long term is a life that is filled with joy, success and happiness. More importantly peace.

If you need to talk to them about something, write down the topic you need to talk to them about. Then write down below what you would say to them:

What I need to talk to my parents about: _____
_____
_____
_____

What do I need from them: _____
_____
_____
_____

What I would say to them: _____
_____
_____
_____

If there is something you need from your parents, or a family member. Call them or arrange a time to speak with them or have lunch with them.

When you do, (this is really important) try to be calm in the way you speak to them. You might wonder why if you are angry or upset, but the first five minutes in any conversation sets the tone. So, try to talk to them calmly. Once you do this, allow them to respond as you listen (really listen to them) who knows, it just might open up the lines of communication and you may find out something new going on with them!

_____

_____

_____

_____

_____

_____

_____

If there is something on your mind, or something you need to say to your parents whether you're 16 or 20 try to find the courage to do so. They are still your parents, if you can't do this now, write down what's going on anyway and come back to this in a few days. If you still cannot do this find someone you trust, who will listen to you, a school counselor, a friend, an Aunt or Uncle, or someone that believes in you...

I already do!

Social Media

We have all seen pictures of a get together where you were not included.

That feeling is the worst. No one wants that to happen to them.

Maybe you saw a post of someone you like and they were at a party or gathering with someone else.

It's like having an arrow go through your heart.

I personally live my life like this.

If I am posting something and my best friend or my parent was watching me I ask myself, would it still be ok to write it?

Turn the tables. If someone posted something similar about you, would you be ok with it?

KINDNESS RULES.

You can never go wrong taking the high road by showing kindness.

How has Social Media impacted you?

I hope in a good way...

Knowing what to avoid in this part of your life may help. Try to be happy for that person. Try to find a way to be happy for their journey... *Your day will come, and your journey will get better. It will!*

Write down three things that could make your life better: Make them areas you can control today, and that you can make happen for a better tomorrow:

1) _____
_____
_____
_____
_____

2) _____
_____
_____
_____
_____
_____

3) _____
_____
_____
_____
_____
_____

If you had one day you could do anything you wanted to do...what would that be?

Write down where you would go, what you would do, and who you would invite?

_____

_____

_____

_____

_____

_____

_____

_____

_____

_____

_____

_____

_____

_____

Is that possible? Could you plan that? It might be a very simple thing to do.

For me, its spending time with my family. One time I went on a vacation, and remember thinking I felt the air being really still and feeling peace...

Secrets

You told your friend a secret and asked them to never tell anyone... and they did...

If that has happened to you, I am so sorry. Sometimes the people we love and trust betray us. It happens, and it's never easy when it happens to you.

This is a reminder that when someone tells you a secret, they believe in you. Be proud of being that kind of friend. The next time someone wants you to gossip or spread rumors... remember how you felt when it happened to you.

When you see this person, how will you act?

What if you were calm and told them how sad it made you feel? Or wrote them a letter? If that person is important to you, sometimes it is better to forgive.

When we forgive someone, we take ourselves out of our own prison. Is there someone that comes to mind after reading this? If so, write how you felt when this happened to you:

_____

_____

_____

_____

_____

_____

_____

_____

_____

_____

Forgiveness

Forgiveness is hard. It's really, really, hard. Sometimes we can forgive immediately, sometimes it takes months, and others years.

Why should we forgive someone?

I know this is hard to understand, but when you don't forgive, you have this ache inside that does not go away. You have this inner resentment and anger that can grow.

You don't want that...

Who could you talk to about forgiveness? A friend, a sibling, a parent, a pastor or a neighbor? You can always make an appointment with a counselor. We could all use counselors in our lifetime...

Write down someone you think is wise and could help you through this:

_____

_____

_____

_____

_____

_____

_____

_____

_____

_____

_____

Not being invited or included in an event or gathering...

Have you ever wanted to go to that event but you weren't invited? That hurts so much. We usually don't tell anyone. Ask yourself, was it really that important to have gone, what did you miss?

_____

_____

_____

_____

_____

_____

_____

_____

_____

_____

_____

_____

_____

_____

_____

When that happens to you, in that very moment, don't stay down, go do something (take a walk, exercise, read a book). They missed out on having the best person at that event as you would have been the life of the party!!!

Exercise is healing...
even with a Jump Rope!

Exercise. If you don't exercise, buy a Jump Rope! Jump as many times as you can, then cool down by taking a walk. I know you don't feel like it... Just go do it. You will be glad you did.

If no one knows you are hurting... YOU have to take care of YOU... please talk with someone. They will be so glad you opened up to them... and you just might help them.

Write down the types of exercises that you could do alone or with a friend:

_____

_____

_____

_____

_____

_____

_____

_____

_____

_____

_____

_____

_____

_____

_____

Everyone hurts at some time in their lifetime...

Expectations

Expectations comes from many sources

People put expectations on our life and sometimes it comes across harsh...

Sometimes its parents, teachers, coaches, employers, siblings and more...

Parents can be hard on us to do better in many areas:

- To keep our room clean
- To help with laundry
- To help with chores like taking out the trash, or mowing the yard

The list goes on...

Where do you feel that type of pressure from?
List out the areas of pressure you feel in your life.

School _____

_____

_____

_____

_____

Home _____

_____

_____

_____

_____

_____

Friends _____

_____

_____

_____

_____

_____

Other areas _____

_____

_____

_____

_____

Here is an example of seeing this in my own family...

"I remember a time when my son was in his first year of College. He came home for the weekend and I was so happy to see him. He wanted to drive my car, and I allowed him to do so. We were singing, acting goofy, and having a blast. My son isn't one for wanting to have long talks so I was getting the quick answers to my questions. I then asked him the following question:

Why did you really sign up for a degree in engineering? His reply? 'I don't know.' I then asked him the question: Did you do this because you felt like you were supposed to be an engineer?

It was like the air stood still and he turned and looked at me. At that moment we both knew.

I explained to him that we will always love him, and that he could be anything in the world he wanted to be. That we would support him in whatever career he chose. I told him that his entire family would love him no matter what.

That took so much pressure off of him. He then switched his degree to an IT engineering focus."

Perhaps something like this
has happened in your life...

Do you feel pressured to be someone that you truly feel you are not? Or pressured to major in a certain degree?

Maybe someone has said the following to you:

"You would be great at _____"

"You should be _____"

"You come from a long history of Physicians, you should follow in this area_____"

Words can have a strong impact or influence on you in your lifetime. Has there been anyone in your life who has made a statement like this to you? If so, write that down below. If you are struggling with that internally, who could you talk to about that? Make a note in your calendar to reach out to that person to help you walk through those feelings, so that you don't carry that internal message with you throughout your lifetime.

_____

_____

_____

_____

_____

_____

_____

_____

_____

In your life, what would you like to do for a career?

Write out some areas that you feel you would be good at in your career:

_____

_____

_____

_____

_____

_____

_____

_____

_____

_____

_____

_____

_____

_____

_____

What do you love? Who do you love?

Write down who you love and why. It could be your Mom, your Dad, your Cat, your Friend? It's important to show empathy to someone, to show that you care. You could be the person who helps that person down the road.

_____

_____

_____

_____

_____

_____

_____

_____

_____

_____

_____

_____

_____

_____

_____

_____

_____

What do you love about each person?

Mom _____

_____

_____

_____

_____

Dad _____

_____

_____

_____

_____

Friend _____

_____

_____

_____

_____

Pet _____

_____

_____

_____

_____

Find a photo of someone you love and paste it here!

When you are so frustrated, what can you do to take out your frustration?

Paste a picture of 1, 2, 3 things you can do
when you are frustrated:

In today's world, there is a lot of uncertainty. What do you feel uncertain about?

_____

_____

_____

_____

_____

_____

What keeps you up at night?

_____

_____

_____

_____

There is a favorite saying of mine, and I hope it helps you:

"What I fear I create" Write down what you fear... Then put it away...

_____

_____

_____

_____

When you are between
life stages...

"What I fear,
I create."

If you connect to any of these statements, write how you feel in the lines provided after you read them.

When you are in middle school, you are ready to be with older students...

_____

_____

_____

When you are in high school, you are ready to graduate and get out...

_____

_____

_____

When you go to a University, College, or Trade School, you may not know what direction you will go...

_____

_____

_____

When you graduate and are starting your future, life may seem uncertain...

_____

_____

_____

Your Future!

When you go to a University, College, or Trade School, you may not know what to major in, or you may change 2 or 3 times... and still question the direction you will go...

When you graduate and are starting your future, life may seem uncertain...

I hope this next page makes you laugh, because this (of all things!!!) was the advice my Mother gave me in my 30's...

Let The Chips Fall!

THAT was her advice on whether I would change careers, etc. At that very moment, the stress was gone, I made a decision and never looked back.

That may not work for you, but that example paints the picture of how much stress we carry around with us. Which then leads to other stressful issues. Primarily our health. Sometimes, you just have to laugh... and overall take care of YOU.

It's ok if you don't know what
to do in life...

Maybe you have no idea what you want to do.

Many successful professionals, athletes, performers, and other senior level executives had no idea what they wanted to do. Many of those individuals failed as well in their lifetime.

However, they started putting one step forward, they did an internship, or took a part-time job in a different field to try something new. What would you do to put that one step forward?

What would you do to put that one step forward?

_____

_____

_____

_____

_____

_____

_____

_____

_____

_____

"A successful Engineer I know thought he wanted to be an Architect. He took a summer job as an Architect, and guess what? He found out it wasn't for him..."

YOU GOT THIS!

Habits

A habit usually takes 28 days to form

I want to

_____

in 28 days

How would your life benefit if you broke/created a habit:

_____

_____

_____

_____

_____

_____

_____

_____

_____

_____

_____

_____

_____

_____

_____

Your Health!

Young adults sometimes do not eat right, exercise, or take the time to breathe.

Take one week for each area and write down one thing you could improve on in your life:

Week One Nutrition. What is one area you could change in your diet? Maybe you could start eating more vegetables. Buy a Vegetable Tray and share it through the week!

_____

_____

_____

_____

_____

_____

_____

_____

_____

_____

Week Two

Exercise. If you already exercise regularly, add a new area to your exercise routine. For instance, if you run, maybe run on a different trail.

_____

_____

_____

_____

_____

_____

_____

_____

_____

_____

_____

_____

_____

_____

_____

_____

_____

_____

_____

Week Three

Family – Do one thing different that could improve your relationship with a sibling or parent.

_____

_____

_____

_____

_____

_____

_____

_____

_____

_____

_____

_____

_____

_____

_____

_____

_____

_____

Week Four

Mental Health – this could be doing yoga, taking walks, practice breathing, or jump roping!

_____

_____

_____

_____

_____

_____

_____

_____

_____

_____

_____

_____

_____

_____

_____

_____

_____

When you are down, disappointed, or just very sad...

Please don't ever try to hurt yourself.

Have a plan of what you could do if you feel this way. Write out the names and numbers of the individuals who come to mind below:

Person I would call:_____

Person I would text: _____

Person I would go see: _____

Person I would write to: _____

Go buy a smoothie. Run in the rain. Lay on the floor, close your eyes, and breathe. Take a deep breath in, and breathe all the way out. Do this 8 times. Put your headphones in and put on happy music or calming music. If people around you are yelling at you, calmly ask them for ten minutes to be alone. If they say no, ask them again in a soft tone. Say to them that you really, really need that ten minutes.

Out of those ideas, do any of those seem like they could work for you? If so, write the ones you like below or underline them so you can reference them when you need to remember what to do.

_____

_____

_____

_____

_____

If you continue to be very sad, please talk with someone. If there is someone you know who will take the time to listen, write them a letter letting them know how special they are to you. If they know you well, create a code word you could use to let them know you really need to talk. Just talk to someone.

Have a plan. Meet that person that day. Let them know. Let them know you need them. They will drop everything when you really need them...

YOU MATTER.

Here are some fun ideas you could do when you are feeling down:

Go get ice cream with a friend!

Dance to happy music alone or with someone!

Write a letter to yourself and list out all of the amazing qualities you have!

Ask a friend to write down 3 great qualities about you. Then write 3 qualities about your friend. Share them with each other and keep yours with you.

Do 10 jumping jacks! Or get with a friend and have a contest to see who can do more jumping jacks!

Clean your room (ok I just had to put that in here for your parents!)

Go for a run!

Listen to music with a friend and see if they can say who the artist is first!

Watch a movie that makes you laugh!

Get enough sleep. Sleep is so important. It's amazing how different you will feel the next day when you get enough sleep the night before.

YOU MATTER.

Disappointment...

We all face disappointment at one point or another in our lifetime...

Maybe your life isn't going the way you thought it would.

I once got some great advice from someone very special to me.

They told me to make a list.

Actually Make Two Lists:

"This is a big one, and one that I can speak from experience on. As a single Mother for ten years, I thought I would never marry again, I thought I would never have the life I have today, sadness consumed me..." That was 10 years ago, and my life could not be better today!!!!

Make a Goal List

Think of everything you want in life, everything you want in High School, College, etc. everything from where you want to go, to what you want to do in the future. What do you want to have accomplished by the time you graduate?

DO. NOT. SETTLE.

Goal List: _____

_____

_____

_____

_____

_____

_____

_____

_____

_____

_____

_____

_____

_____

_____

_____

_____

_____

_____

_____

_____

_____

_____

_____

_____

_____

Make a Friend List

List out all of the qualities you would want In a friend. Compare this list to your current friends. Do they match?

Friend List: _____

_____

_____

_____

_____

_____

_____

_____

_____

_____

_____

_____

_____

_____

_____

_____

_____

_____

_____

_____

_____

_____

_____

_____

_____

Anxiety is real.

It happens to many people. When you feel like you are having a panic attack, do something different to distract yourself away from what you are doing in that moment.

What is something you could do to distract yourself when you are having a panic attack? Write that down so you can reference it in the future.

_____

_____

_____

_____

_____

_____

_____

_____

_____

_____

_____

_____

_____

_____

_____

_____

_____

This is YOUR life...don't let those moments take over your life!

I hope you have enjoyed this journal as much as I have when putting this together for you. I could write forever but for now here are a few topics I want to leave you with...

Bullying & Cyber Bullying – both are cruel and unacceptable. If this is happening to you, I am so sorry. This should never happen to anyone. If this is happening to you, please talk to someone at your school, your family or through resources in the back of this journal.

Dating – This is a big one.

If they don't like you, move on. I have a theory that's never done me wrong.

"If they don't want to be with me, I don't want to be with them period. If they don't want to be with you, it's their loss period."

Lying – The truth usually comes out. One lie leads to another, then another, then another. Trust is something that takes a very long time to build. Lying can take that trust away immediately. It take's a very long time to rebuild that trust in someone you have lied to.

YOUR LIFE...

Friends – Surround yourself with people who make you a better person.

Your life will be amazing. If you hang with people who lift you up, you have their back and they have yours. Your life will be full of richness that money cannot buy. Look back at your "friends list" to remind yourself of the qualities that you need in your life from good friends.

YOU GOT THIS!

YOU CAN DO THIS.

YOU ARE STRONGER THAN YOU THINK.

THERE ARE PEOPLE WHO BELIEVE IN YOU.

THERE ARE PEOPLE WHO DEPEND ON YOU.

YOU ARE TALENTED.

YOU ARE BEAUTIFUL INSIDE AND OUT.

YOU MATTER.

COMPLETION

When you have finished this journal, sign your name here and date it. One day you will look back on this and be proud of your journey. I can't wait to hear how your journey goes! We would love to hear from you! Feel free to write us at info@time2refocus.com

Name	Date

I am already proud of you!!!!
Angela Stephens

Resources to contact

These are resources that we have come across that may prove helpful to you. Please understand, we ARE NOT recommending or endorsing any of them. It is up to you to determine if they offer something you need and whether or not it is appropriate for your situation.

Abuse
National Domestic Violence Hotline:
1-800-799-7233

Rape, Sexual Assault, Abuse, and Incest National Network (RAINN):
1-800-656-HOPE

Alcohol
Al-Anon for Families of Alcoholics:
Automated meeting information
1-800-344-2666

Alcoholics Anonymous:
aa.org

National Council on Alcohol and Drugs:
www.ncadd.org

Anxiety/Panic
Panic Disorder Information Hotline:
1-800-64-PANIC

Bipolar and Depression
Depression and Bipolar Support Alliance (DBSA):
http://www.dbsalliance.org/

Chronic Pain
American Chronic Pain Association:
http://www.theacpa.org/

Cyber Bullying
www.stopbullying.gov
www.cyberbullying.org
www.stopoutbullying.org

Domestic Violence
National Domestic Violence Hotline:
1-800-799-SAFE (24 hrs)
https://www.thehotline.org/

Learning Disabilities and ADHD
Children & Adults with Attention Deficit/Hyperactivity Disorder
Resource Center (CHADD):
1-800-233-4050

National Center for Learning Disabilities:
1-888-575-7373

Resources for ADHD & ADHD families:
additudemag.com

Sexual Assault
Rape, Sexual Assault, Abuse, and Incest National Network (RAINN):
1-800-656-HOPE

National Domestic Violence Hotline / Child Abuse / Sexual Abuse:
1-800-799-7233

Substance Abuse
SAMHSA's National Helpline:
1-800-662-4357

National Institute on Drug Abuse Hotline:
1-800-662-4357

Suicide
National Suicide Prevention Lifeline:
1-800-273-8255 (1-800-273-TALK)

National Hopeline Network:
1-800-784-2433 (1-800-SUICIDE)

Mental Health America:
1-800-969-6642
www.mentalhealthamerica.net

National Alliance on Mental Illness:
1-800-950-NAMI (6264)
www.nami.org

Women's Law
Provides basic legal information referrals, and emotional
support for victims of abuse:
https://hotline.womenslaw.org/

Pregnancy
Planned Parenthood Hotline:
1-800-230-PLAN (7526)

Notes

Our Passion is Helping People!

We are rooting for you!

The team at RE-Focus, The Creative Office

www.time2refocus.com